Peppa Pig

Nursery Rhyme Time!

This little piggy

This little piggy went to market,
This little piggy stayed at home.
This little piggy had roast beef,
This little piggy had none,
And this little piggy cried
wee, wee, wee
all the way home.

Polly, put the kettle on

Polly, put the kettle on,
Polly, put the kettle on,
Polly, put the kettle on,
We'll all have tea.

Sukey, take it off again,
Sukey, take it off again,
Sukey, take it off again,
They've all gone away.

Ring-a-ring o'roses

Ring-a-ring o'roses,
A pocket full of posies.
A-tishoo! A-tishoo!
We all fall down.

Hey diddle diddle

Hey diddle diddle,
The cat and the fiddle,
The cow jumped over
the moon;
The little dog laughed
To see such fun,
And the dish ran away
With the spoon.

Mary, Mary, quite contrary

Mary, Mary,
quite contrary,
How does your
garden grow?
With silver bells and
cockle shells,
And pretty maids
all in a row.

Mary had a little lamb

Mary had a little lamb,
Its fleece was white as snow;
And everywhere
that Mary went,
The lamb was sure to go.

Pat-a-cake, pat-a-cake

Pat-a-cake, pat-a-cake,
baker's man.
Bake me a cake
as fast as you can.
Pat it and prick it
and mark it with 'B'.
And put in the oven
for baby and me.

Miss Polly had a dolly

Miss Polly had a dolly
who was sick, sick, sick.
So she called for the doctor
to come quick, quick, quick.
The doctor came with
his bag and his hat,
And he knocked on the door
with a rat-a-tat-tat.

Old King Cole

Old King Cole
was a merry old soul
And a merry old soul was he.
He called for his pipe,
And he called for his bowl,
And he called
for his fiddlers three.

Twinkle, twinkle, little star

Twinkle, twinkle, little star,
How I wonder what you are.
Up above the world so high,
Like a diamond in the sky.
Twinkle, twinkle, little star,
How I wonder what you are.